Henry VIII's departure for France in 1520. Both cast and wrought ordnance are mounted in the Dover blockhouse and in the ships, where lidded ports reveal big guns.

NAVAL CANNON

John Munday

Shire Publications Ltd

CONTENTS

Published in 1998 by Shire Publications Ltd, Cromwell House, Church Street, Princes Risborough, Buckinghamshire HP27 9AA, UK. Copyright © 1987 by John Munday. First published 1987; reprinted 1998. Shire Album 186. ISBN 0 85263 844 2.

Printed in Great Britain by CIT Printing Services, Press Buildings, Merlins Bridge, Haverfordwest, Pembrokeshire SA61 1XF.

British Library Cataloguing in Publication Data: Munday, John. Naval cannon. - (Shire album; 186). 1. Ordnance, Naval – History. I. Title. 632.4'18'09. VF15. ISBN 0-85263-844-2.

ACKNOWLEDGEMENTS
The author records his grateful thanks to the Trustees and Director of the National Maritime Museum for permission to reproduce the cover picture and the majority of the illustrations from the collections at Greenwich. For other illustrations he is much indebted to Dr Margaret Rule CBE, FSA, the Mary Rose Trust (page 5, both pictures), and to the late Captain John Wells CBE, DSC, RN, the Warrior Preservation Trust (page 31), while the illustrations on pages 6, 7, 15, 19 (lower) and 25 (centre) are from the author's own collection. Most valuable advice is acknowledged from Howard L. Blackmore FSA, formerly Deputy Master of the Royal Armouries, from David J. Lyon MA, formerly of the National Maritime Museum, from Philip G. W. Annis FSA, and from Major J. G. D. Elvin TD, RA.

COVER: *This detail from 'Nelson Falling', a painting by Denis Dighton, shows Victory's quarter-deck 12 pdrs, the nearer being loaded and primed by powder-horn, the other firing. The powder boy with cased cartridge is wounded.*

BELOW: *A wrought iron gun from Mary Rose, recovered in 1836. It is a stone-thrower of 8 inch (20 cm) bore with a spare chamber, one surviving truck and a solid bed or carriage.*

Marked with the Tudor rose and crown, which was also used in Stuart times, this early 24 pdr iron gun (not originally an English weight), came from the Matthias, a Dutch prize sunk in the river Medway in 1667. It is now on an iron garrison carriage. (Greenwich Hospital Collection.)

INTRODUCTION

The word 'cannon' described a size of gun and was the size next to the largest, the cannon royal. Guns are *ordnance* and there is brass ordnance (technically bronze) and iron ordnance, made for both land service and sea service. Artillery, on the other hand, originally included the great catapults of the Romans and also long bows, cross bows and hand guns. In the eleventh century the Chinese had gunpowder for bombs and guns appeared towards the end of the thirteenth century. In Europe, Friar Bacon undoubtedly wrote of gunpowder about the middle of the thirteenth century and the first guns were fired in the early years of the fourteenth century. At sea, since naval warfare consisted of *boarding* (putting ships side by side) and *entering* (swarming on to an enemy's deck), early guns were anti-personnel weapons of different sizes. From ships' stern and fore castles, *murdering pieces* discharged all

manner of shot.

Great Britain is supremely fortunate in being able to exhibit three old ships of war which between them cover the whole story of the smooth-bore ship gun, the key to sea power for some 350 years.

Within Portsmouth harbour, a royal dockyard was established by Henry VII and fortified by Henry VIII. Today it houses HM Naval Base Portsmouth and the Naval Heritage Centre. Since 1928 the first-rate line of battle ship HMS *Victory* has been open to visitors there. With the help of the Society for Nautical Research she was restored to the condition in which she fought at the Battle of Trafalgar on 21st October 1805, when she flew the St George's flag of Vice-Admiral Lord Nelson. Launched in 1765, she had already carried many famous admirals as a flagship, mounting over a hundred guns of different sizes. In 1922 she was put into dry dock, where she is still in full commis-

3

sion, wearing the flag of the Commander in Chief, Naval Home Command.

In 1982, the Tudor warship *Mary Rose* was raised from the silt of the sea bed off Southsea Castle where she had lain since her accidental sinking in the face of an invading French fleet in 1545, watched by Henry VIII. The imposing remains of her hull are being conserved by the Mary Rose Trust, also in the Naval Base. Among the 16,000 registered finds recovered were most of her starboard guns complete with carriages and ancillary equipment providing superb examples from the infancy of naval gunnery.

Through the dedication of the Warrior Preservation Trust and the Hartlepool yard where she was restored, the famous ironclad steamship HMS *Warrior* and her guns can also be seen. Built on the Thames in 1860, she was, at the time of her commissioning, a match for any fleet, let alone any ship, afloat. With her guns the scope of this book is completed, for the later development of enormous rifled muzzle-loaders and huge breech-loaders is another story.

THE GREAT GUNS

Early guns fired stone shot, as did the older siege machines, the ballista and the trebuchet. At the end of Henry VIII's reign his navy list enumerated *Gonnes of Brasse, Gonnes of Yron, Shotte of Yron* and *Shotte of Stoen and Leade* and among the king's men were *Souldiers, Marriners* and *Gonners* in proportion. Of the latest costly brass ordnance, his *Mary Rose* is listed as mounting two cannon, two demi-cannon, two culverins, six demi-culverins, two sakers and a falcon. The various *natures* of gun (a gunner's term) were later known by the weight of shot they fired so her guns could be listed as two 60 pounders (pdrs), two 30 pdrs, two 20 pdrs, six 10 pdrs, two 5 pdrs and one 2½ pdr. These sizes are very approximate for rarely do two authorities agree about dimensions and weights.

Bronzefounders, masters at casting great bells and pounding mortars, took easily enough to guns. The noble metal lent itself to decoration and, in the bellfounding tradition, guns bore the names of their makers, ornament in relief and the coats of arms of their owners, as befitted the expensive products of master craftsmen. Their technology was well advanced, but guns were loaded at the mouth, the *muzzle*.

Iron guns were blacksmith's work; satisfactory castings could not be produced so bars of iron were welded together to form a tube and rings were shrunk over it, as hoops on to a *barrel*. These guns were breech-loaders, for to stop up one end of the barrel a separate section, the chamber to receive gunpowder, was wedged in at the rear by a block or quoin against the massive end of the bed or carriage. Chambers could be changed quite readily, so these iron guns were probably fired with comparative rapidity. A surviving account book of the Keeper of the King's Ships in 1422 shows the *Holy Ghost of the Tower* as having six cannon and twelve chambers, while the *Great Mary* had three cannon and nine chambers.

While soldiers were developing their cannon for *battery,* the idea of arming ships with similar weapons had been germinating. To have a weapon which would inflict damage on an enemy hull became the gunner's purpose and larger guns joined the murdering pieces. The idea of a ship as a floating battery for attack and defence not only influenced the shape of ships and their structure but also their handling.

Henry VIII bought guns from the foundries of Europe, from the famous Poppenruyter of Mechlin for example, but he also encouraged gunfounding in England and brought the Arcana family from Italy to work for him in London. He also employed the Frenchman Pierre Baude to cast guns at Houndsditch (where he was known as Bawood). Coming after all these foreigners, John and Robert Owen proudly inscribed their beautiful bronze guns with their names and 'Sons of an English' (man). In the

Mary Rose's brass culverin-bastard, raised in 1979. Its bore is 4¾ inches (12.1 cm), its length 25 calibres. It is inscribed 'Robert and John Owyn Bretheryn Borne in the Citye of London the sonnes of an English made thys Bastard Anno Dni 1537'.

Weald of Kent and Sussex, the iron district, foundries were established where smelting fuel was plentiful and King Henry lived to see iron guns successfully cast.

Putting big guns into ships was a matter for the shipwrights; doors or *ports* in a hull were not new, but the different natures of guns needed tailored carriages and gun ports. Weight had to be distributed evenly and placed as low as possible, so perhaps it was the stability of the *Mary Rose,* as re-armed and brought up to date at the end of Henry's reign, which was at fault and contributed to her loss. She carried a mixed armament of wrought iron guns of the apparently primitive sort, as well as superb brass pieces only two or three years old, and she marks a stage in the evolution of the warship. She was also one of the first to have her sides pierced for carrying guns on more than one deck. Evidently she carried one cannon royal, one of the Owen brothers' pieces, for it was recovered in 1836 and is 8 feet 6 inches long (2.6 m) with a bore or *calibre* of 8½ inches (21.6 cm), throwing a 66 pdr round-shot. This is a cannon for battery, of 12 calibres in length, but there was a class of gun longer in relation to the bore, the culverin family (from the Latin *colubra,* French *couleuvre,* a snake), which could measure 30 or more calibres.

A gunner's linstock from Mary Rose. It 'is a handsome carved stick, more than halfe a yard long, with a Cocke at one end to hold fast his Match' (Captain John Smith).

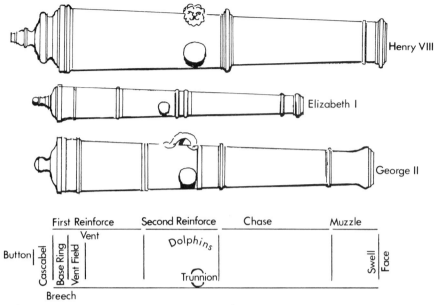

	First Reinforce			Second Reinforce	Chase	Muzzle

Typical profiles, brass guns, not to scale.

Button | Cascabel | Base Ring | Vent Field | Vent | Dolphins | Trunnion | Swell | Face

Breech

ABOVE: *Typical profiles, brass guns, not to scale.*

BELOW: *Typical profiles, iron guns, not to scale. The faceted early style occurs also in brass. The ring for the breech rope was cast on the cascabel from the eighteenth century. The ring through the button with the 'gate' was introduced in the mid nineteenth century.*

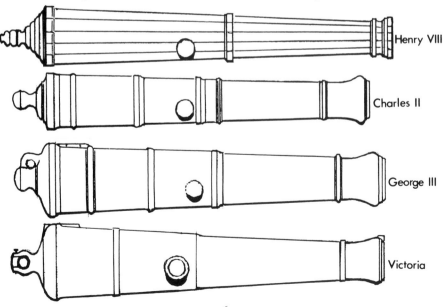

6

There was a baffling variety of sizes: culverins divided into the ordinary, the extra-ordinary (longer) and the bastard (shorter) as well as demi-culverins and their kin, the sakers and minions, all of which carried a smaller shot further than the cannon. There was also the cannon petro or petriero, which still fired a stone shot, a gunstone, and was only about 8 calibres; it was considered an effective weapon 'to shoot near at hand'.

Small guns on forks or swivels, some of them cleverly devised breech-loaders with their chambers like tankards with handles, to be filled and clamped into place, were also part of ships' ordnance. Guns came to be made according to rules of proportion; for example, the *trunnions* (the supporting stubs) were placed at $4/7$ of the length from the muzzle, while the 'metal about the breech' (the circumference) was 9 calibres, round the trunnions 7 calibres and at the muzzle 5 calibres. In cast guns the chamber where the *charge* of powder was exploded had to be the stoutest part of the piece. Sighting along the top of the gun was therefore no use as the true axis ran through the centre of the bore. Even the earliest gunnery books explain how to *dispart* a piece, that is, to find the difference between the semi-diameters at muzzle and breech and so establish a true line of sight.

The charge was put into the chamber by a *ladle* of copper on a long handle, a measure in fact, but cartridges of paper were an early invention and much more handy on board ship, so then the ladle came into use only when the supply of cartridges ran out. The round-shot had to be fairly loose in the bore or it was impossible to load and if it jammed on firing the gun might explode. The difference between diameters of shot and bore was called the *windage*. This allowed the flash to ignite an explosive shell, when such were being fired, but if it was too great the gases of the explosion leaked round the shot. *Wads* made of old rope, wood or anything handy would plug the bore and were introduced with the powder and shot. They were shoved home with a long-handled *rammer* or with a stout rope, tightly twisted and having a wooden rammer head, and which pro-

Types of shot. Chain, bar, etc, were designed to cut the rigging and damage masts and spars. Langridge, case and grape shot were anti-personnel. 'Langridge ... like unto a lanthern full of pobble stones, dice shot, musket bullets, pieces of iron or suchlike will doe great execution.'

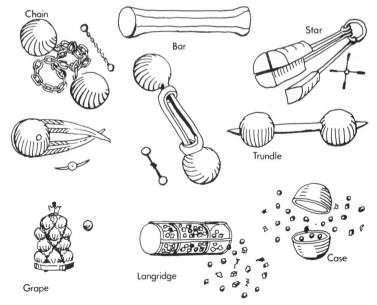

A gun and a gunner with his tools. In the centre is a rule with folding points for calipers. Note the coiled rope rammer as well as the ladle and 'spunge'. From John Seller, 1691.

vided a flexible and more convenient alternative. At sea the guns were kept loaded with one wad between cartridge and shot and another after the shot. In action only the wad after the shot was used.

When ready to fire, the gunner pierced the cartridge by driving his *priming iron* down the *vent*, which he then filled with special powder. *Fire* was given to the charge by a *slow-match*, a glowing end of impregnated rope held at arm's length in a cleft stick called a *linstock* and applied to the *touch-hole* at the top of the vent. Because of the windage the actual flight of the shot depended on how it glanced out of the barrel, so shooting at other than close range was not accurate. The

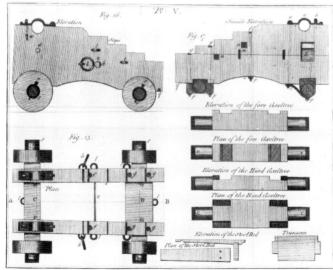

Sea-service carriage: the sturdy jointing had to withstand the shock of explosion and recoil. Muller's improved design; engraving from his 'Treatise of Artillery', 1768.

8

rear end of the gun tapered into the *cascabel* (not included in a gun's measurement), ending in the *button* or *pommelion*.

The carriage supported the gun balanced on its trunnions; by elevating the muzzle the shot would fly higher, and by increasing the charge it would travel further. Beneath the breech end *quoins* or wedges were inserted on the *bed*. Originally the carriage was built on a complete base or bed, the side pieces, known as *cheeks* or *brackets*, rising from it; later, *axle trees*, a *transom* and a *stool-bed* replaced the base. The cheeks were fashioned in steps at the rear so that handspikes could be inserted to lever up the heavy breech end, to adjust the quoin. The carriage had small wooden wheels, *trucks*, larger at the fore end because the ship's deck had a camber, and on these the gun was hauled out for firing. The discharge also caused it to *recoil*, to drive backwards on its trucks, and it was restrained by the large breeching rope round the cascabel and secured to the ship's side.

Guns were *trained* to left or right by leverage of the handspikes and by hauling on the *side tackles*. After firing, the barrel had to be cleared in case smouldering fragments ignited the next charge prematurely, for which a wet *sponge* of lambskin on a long staff and also a *worm*, a double spiral hook, were used.

FROM DRAKE TO NELSON

In the summer of 1588 the Invincible Armada of Spain sailed to invade England and, for the first time in British history on so large a scale, massed armed ships sailed against an invader, fighting their guns at varying ranges in a variety of weather. However, the guns of the English fleet were not the deciding factor. It was the handiness of its ships and the seamanship of its commanders, although they nearly ran out of gunpowder! The Spaniards had equally good armament and more of it. Howard, the Queen's Lord Admiral in the *Ark Royal*, mounted four demi-cannon, four cannon perrier, ten culverins, ten demi-culverins, six sakers and two falcons, totalling with other pieces about fifty, in other words eight pieces for battery and the rest lighter, longer range guns.

One problem was that a ship as a gun platform was always in motion, so that unless the gun was so close that the shot could not miss, the chance of inflicting serious damage on the enemy was uncertain. It needed great skill and judgement to score a hit and books were written to help. William Bourne wrote, in *The Arte of Shooting in Great Ordnaunce* (1578), 'I am so bold to be the first Englishman that put forth any book as touching these causes...' and his first chapter was 'How to know the Goodnesse or Badnesse of Powder'. When to fire was another prob- lem – on the upward or the downward roll? Bourne again: '...if you shoote when the other Ship is aloft on the top of the Sea, you have a bigger marke.... there is no better time for to give fire than when shee is beginning to rise upon the Sea'.

Captain John Smith, the English colonist of Virginia, saved by Princess Pocahontas, published his useful *Accidence for Young Seamen* (later appearing as the *Seaman's Grammar*) in 1626. He lists faults in guns: 'honey-combed...when she is ill cast or overmuch worn she will be rugged within, which is dangerous...any rag of her wadding being afire and sticking there, may fire the next charge you put in her'. The moulds for cast guns contained a solid core which gave the piece its bore, but this method was somewhat hazardous for the least variation in alignment of the core would make the gun uncertain to sight and in practice most pieces turned out to be individuals. The careful gunner surveyed all his guns, checked, measured, probed and calculated, and if the answers were below standard 'you cannot suffer their true proportion' (of powder) 'either at Proof or Action'.

In the seventeenth century the first big development was James I's *Prince Royal* (1610), the first warship to have guns on three decks. Charles I's

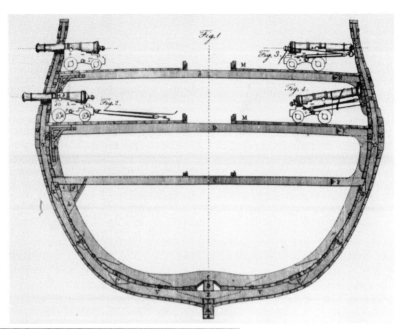

ABOVE: *A drawing from Falconer's 'Dictionary of the Marine', 1769. Fig. 2 is a gun with train tackle to hold it back; fig. 3 is a gun with side tackle; fig. 4 is a gun secured for sea.*

LEFT: *A calibre compass or gunner's rule, 'made by Heath and Wing in the Strand London', about 1760. The weight of shot was read off at the head. On the reverse the weight of powder charges and other information were given.*

Half-section model of a first-rate like the Royal George showing the placing of carriage guns.

Sovereign of the Seas (1637) had her great guns on three levels, continuous from bow to stern, the smaller calibres uppermost. At the king's command she mounted 102 guns, all cast brass pieces, engraved and ornamented. On the lower tier were twenty cannon drakes (drake being a lighter form of gun) and eight demi-cannon drakes; the middle tier had twenty-four culverin drakes and six culverins; the upper tier had twenty demi-culverin drakes and two demi-culverins. On the fo'c'sle there were eight demi-culverin drakes, on the half-deck six and on the quarter-deck two, with two culverin drakes up for'ad as well. As gunpowder manufacture improved, long guns could become shorter, a decided advantage on board ship for a culverin could measure 13 feet (3.9 m).

The second half of the seventeenth

A gun made by John Browne, 1640, bearing the cipher and crown of Charles I. A 2¹/₂ pdr, but short, it is traditionally supposed to be from the ship Sovereign of the Seas.

century saw the great fleets of the English and the Dutch in conflict at sea, with enormous fire-power and equal determination on both sides; the days of Blake and Tromp were followed by those of James, Duke of York, and de Ruyter, of Monck, Sandwich and the younger Tromp.

Captured Dutch guns were found to fire shot of 24 pounds (10.8 kg) and 12 pounds (5.4 kg), sizes not found in the English arsenal, so some guns began to be known by their weight of shot instead of the old names.

The number of cast iron guns was increasing. The *Swiftsure* of 1665 mounted sixty brass and twelve iron pieces but by 1700 only three-deckers carried all brass ordnance. The *Royal Charles* and the *Royal James,* three-decked first-rates of the 1670s, mounted twenty-six whole cannon or demi-cannon, firing 42 pdr and 32 pdr shot respectively, then twenty-eight 24 pdrs and the same number of 9 pdrs and finally fourteen 5 pdrs. Admiral Sir Cloudesley Shovel was wrecked among the Isles of Scilly in 1707. Divers have recovered from the wreck site some fine French brass guns. Captured ordnance was taken as trophies of war, sometimes used and sometimes sent for melting down.

The Board of Ordnance, presided over by the Master-General, saw to the provision of guns for both army and navy. In 1716 their master gunfounder Andrew Schalch began production in their new Royal Brass Foundry at Woolwich on the Thames. His name appears on guns, mortars and howitzers until 1770, when J. and P. Verbruggen, father and son, took over. The names of J. and H. King are found on brass pieces cast there from 1785 until 1813. All the Crown's brass ordnance also bore the crest or cipher of the Master-General of the time. A Swiss gunfounder, Maritz, had perfected machinery for the horizontal boring out of *massive* cast brass guns. Massive or solid casting produced fewer imperfections and the improved machinery produced guns that were true-bored. In Britain the techniques were applied successfully and eventually in 1776 solid-cast iron guns were ordered to be made for the services.

A feathered arrow in flight spins, boring straight to its mark, whereas a round-shot from a gun clearly did not. Mr Benjamin Robins, inventor, wrote his *New Principles of Gunnery* in 1742 and prophesied that, as had been demonstrated on the musket, *rifling* or spiral grooving in the barrel would be the answer for the great guns. Accuracy and a greater range would be attained and

A brass-cased flintlock, fired by a pull on the lanyard. It replaced match and linstock though these were held in reserve against mechanical failure.

Portrayed standing by a gun fitted with a flint-lock is Rear-Admiral Sir Charles Douglas Bt, its whole-hearted proponent, as he was of the goose-quill primer. Ingeniously fashioned and filled, this was only 2¹/₂ inches (6 cm) long but when ignited sent a 6 inch (15 cm) stab of flame into the cartridge.

gunners, like archers, could shoot and be confident of hitting the target. The use of an elongated projectile was another of Mr Robins's proposals and the great sailor and administrator Admiral Lord Anson is known to have compared notes with him. In 1755 Anson ordered flint-locks, as used to ignite muskets and pistols, to be supplied for the quarter-deck guns, the lightest pieces in the fleet. Cartridges were to be made of flannel, which burnt up entirely, instead of paper, which did not, and priming powder was to be supplied in small tin tubes for insertion in the vent. However, these innovations, orders from on high though they were, seem to have lapsed.

Other inventive men were dissatisfied with naval gunnery as it was. Captain Charles Douglas of HM Ship *Duke* in 1778 had such confidence in the efficacy of the flint-lock for firing cannon that he equipped his ship with them out of his own purse when the Navy forbore to sup-

ply. He recognised the superiority of flannel cartridges and developed priming tubes of quill filled with a hardened explosive paste which was safer, tidier and more certain than loose powder from a powder-horn. Douglas became captain of Lord Rodney's flagship HMS *Formidable* and in April 1782 he was able to demonstrate his superior rate of fire and hitting power in the victory over the French at The Saints in the West Indies.

Improvements also came from the Board of Ordnance, from artillerists like General Thomas Blomefield, who introduced a gun with an increased weight of metal about the breech and reduced metal in the chase which, with bigger charges, gave increased range. He is also remembered for having achieved acceptable standards in the quality of iron ordnance supplied by contractors.

The *Royal George* first-rate of 100 guns, launched in 1756, was equipped

ABOVE: *This iron 24 pdr bears King George III's cipher. Now on an iron garrison carriage, its extreme range at 10 degrees of elevation was about 2640 yards (2410m). (Greenwich Hospital Collection.)*

BELOW: *HMS Victory at sea: a painting by Monamy Swaine, 1793. The lower-deck ports are closed against the sea. The chequered painting of the sides with dark port lids, called 'Nelson-fashion', dated from about 1801.*

HMS Victory, port bow view. The 12 pdr upper-deck guns have no port lids. The 24 pdrs on the middle deck and 32 pdrs on the lower deck are staggered.

with all brass ordnance including 42 pdrs on the lower deck. By 1780 the latter had been replaced by lighter iron pieces to lessen the burden on her ageing hull. After her celebrated accidental loss off Portsmouth in 1782 her valuable guns were mostly salvaged; some were also recovered in 1836-40 and the bronze from them made into souvenir model guns.

HMS *Victory's* armament in 1805 was fifteen 32 pdrs to each broadside on the lower deck and the same number of 24 pdrs on the middle deck. With fourteen 24 pdrs a side on the upper deck and seven 12 pdrs a side on the quarter-deck, she mounted 102 guns. These were supplemented by a pair of *carronades* on her fo'c'sle firing 68 pdr shot, but such weapons were not counted among her guns, as will later appear. Lord Nelson, when asked in 1801 about a new idea for sighting and laying the guns, wrote: 'As to the plan for pointing a gun truer than we do at present, if the person comes I shall of course look at it, or be happy, if necessary to use it, but I hope we shall be able to get so close to our enemies that our shot cannot miss the object'. This was not just the intrepid admiral crying 'death or victory', it was practical sense to avoid wasting powder and shot. It has been remarked that at the Battle of Copenhagen in that year Nelson's squadron did little damage to the Danish installations on shore because it was not able to lay the guns with accuracy by the old method.

ABOVE: *A brass 24 pdr cast by Andrew Schalch in 1743, recovered from the Royal George, wrecked in 1782. Lent by the Royal Armouries to Southsea Castle, it is 10 feet 3 inches (312 cm) in overall length.*

BELOW: *Queen Victoria's cipher is on the chase of this iron 32 pdr of 1859. The foundry mark 'Low Moor' (Yorkshire) is on the trunnion. The weight, 59 cwt (2997 kg), is stamped on the breech ring.*

HMS Victory's lower gun deck looking aft. Sailors lived (messed) between the guns. The corner of a mess table shows at lower right.

GUNNERS AND GUNNERY

The Captain had his lieutenants, the commissioned officers. The Gunner, like the Master, the Bo's'n and the Carpenter, was a warrant officer and with his Mates was responsible under the Captain for the magazines, the guns, the stores of shot and equipment, the small arms, the side arms and the pikes and axes. He lived in the Gunroom, aft on the lower deck. Being such a trustworthy man, he also looked after the youngest officers, the midshipmen and volunteers, which is why even today the junior mess is called the Gunroom. In 1578 Bourne wrote : 'and the principallest thing is that, that he that is at the Helme must be sure to steere steady and bee ruled by him that giveth the levell, and he that giveth fire must be nimble and ready at a suddaine'- so the gunner had to be a good seaman too.

One man to every 500 pounds (227 kg) of metal was the old saying and the crew of a 32 pdr 59 cwt (2997 kg) gun was thirteen men. It was not intended that both broadsides should be fully manned; in action, if a ship had to fight both sides, each gun's crew would have two guns to look after, to serve. Number 2 starboard gun's crew would move to number 1 port-side gun, or perhaps half of a crew would move across. Crews would be depleted by casualties in action and drills were designed to make every man thoroughly familiar with every duty of each *number,* as the gun's crew members were called. Number 1 was the captain of the gun, number 2 the second captain, 3 and 4 were loader and sponger, 5, 6 and 7, 8 manned the side or quarter tackles for running the gun out and, in keeping with the rudimentary appliances in wooden ships, every operation was performed by bent back and sweat of brow. Numbers 9 and 10 were handspike men, 11 and 12 saw to the priming and supplied the shot and wads, but number 13 did only one thing: as powderman he had to

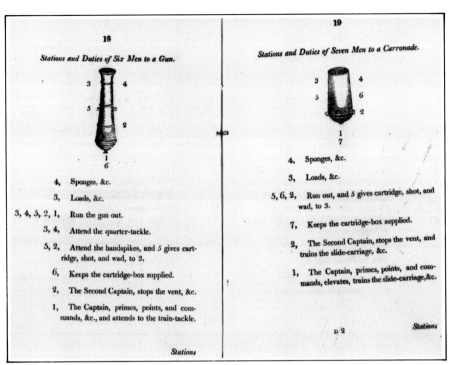

Stations and Duties of Six Men to a Gun.

4, Sponges, &c.

3, Loads, &c.

3, 4, 5, 2, 1, Run the gun out.

3, 4, Attend the quarter-tackle.

5, 2, Attend the handspikes, and 5 gives cart-ridge, shot, and wad, to 3.

6, Keeps the cartridge-box supplied.

2, The Second Captain, stops the vent, &c.

1, The Captain, primes, points, and com-mands, &c., and attends to the train-tackle.

Stations

Stations and Duties of Seven Men to a Carronade.

4, Sponges, &c.

3, Loads, &c.

5, 6, 2, Run out, and 5 gives cartridge, shot, and wad, to 3.

7, Keeps the cartridge-box supplied.

2, The Second Captain, stops the vent, and trains the slide-carriage, &c.

1, The Captain, primes, points, and com-mands, elevates, trains the slide-carriage, &c.

D 2   *Stations*

A gun's crew numbered (from the Admiralty's 'Exercise of the Great Guns', 1818), showing a skeleton crew of six, just sufficient to work a long gun, and a carronade's crew, which could be only three.

'keep the cartridge box supplied'. Even at half crew the last man was powder-man; the captain of the gun hauled with the rest in addition to priming, pointing, attending the train tackle and generally giving orders.

The Admiralty first issued *The Exercise of the Great Guns* in the mid eighteenth century, but whether it was possible to maintain the routine in the heat of a fight depended on the Captain's belief in drill and keeping his lieutenants up to the mark. By the time Nelson was at sea the sequence of gunnery orders had been reduced from forty to fourteen: 1 Silence. 2 Cast loose your guns. 3 Level your guns. 4 Take out your *tompions* (muzzle plugs). 5 Run out your guns. 6 Prime. 7 Point your guns. 8 Fire. 9 Sponge your guns. 10 Load with cartridge. 11 Shot your guns. 12 Put in your tompions. 13 House your guns. 14 Secure.

After the end of the Napoleonic war the book gives just twelve orders, with a slightly different emphasis: 1 Clear for ac-tion. 2 Cast loose the guns. 3 Run out the guns. 4 Prick the cartridge. 5 Prime. 6 Point. 7 Make ready. 8 Fire. 9 Stop the vent. 10 Sponge. 11 Load. 12 Secure the guns. Vital in the sequence was order 9, 'Stop the vent'. A plug was forced in 'the *instant* the gun is fired....to smother any spark of fire that may remain in the cham-ber'. Strangely this order is omitted after order 8 ('Fire') in the earlier set. Perhaps they learnt from accidents!

Gunners continued to write useful handbooks, manuals of gunnery in the manner of Bourne and 'Virginia' Smith. Captain Robert Park of Ipswich wrote his *Defensive War by Sea* (1704) for mer-chantmen, for every ship had some sort of armament against pirates and prowl-ers. Park was a candid and conversa-tional writer on the practicalities and his information was used by later writers, notably William Mountaine, whose *Sea-man's Vade Mecum or Defensive War by Sea* came out in 1747, the same year as his *Practical Sea-Gunner's Companion*.

In 1777 William Hutchinson, who said

(40)	
Words of Command.	**Obſervations.**

24.

Spunge the Gun.

> In ſpunging the Gun, the Spunge is to be drawn backwards and forwards two or three Times, as well as puſhed home ſtrongly, and in taking it out, turn it round two or three Times in the Gun. Obſerve to ſtrike your Spunge well on the Muzzle of the Gun, to cleanſe it. If you make uſe of a Rope Spunge, obſerve to ſhift Ends, and have your Rammer Head at Hand.

25.

Handle the Car-
tridge.

26.

Put it into the
Gun.

> You muſt put the Cartridge in as far as you can reach with your Arm, the lower End firſt, and Seam of the Cartridge downwards.
> 27. Wad

(41)	
Words of Command.	**Obſervations.**

27.

Wad to your
Cartridge.

28.

Handle the
Rammer.

29.

Ram home Wad
and Cartridge.

> Obſerve to give two or three Strokes, to ram it well home.

30.

Unſtop the
Touch-hole.

F 2   31. H ndle

ABOVE: 'Exercise of the Great Guns', an Admiralty handbook of about 1750, contains forty separate orders with detailed instructions. 'Observe to' means 'make sure to'.

RIGHT: 'Cast loose your guns', the first order in the drill book. This Victorian illustration by W. H. Overend reconstructs a gun's crew of Nelson's day.

19

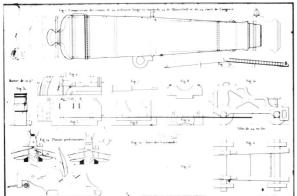

TOP: *Baron Dupin's 'Voyage dans La Grande Bretagne' (Paris, 1826) compares types of guns and shows Howard Douglas's double-flinted locks, mortars and beds and an iron carriage.*

CENTRE: *Secured for sea: a model gun with its muzzle lashed above the port. A 3-ton gun on wheels was best kept tightly in check at sea.*

BOTTOM: *One of Major General Congreve's 'Sights or Instruments for Pointing Guns;' described in his booklet of 1818. An early cross-wire fore-sight, it is stamped 'Enfield'.*

HMS Superb, eighty guns, about 1845. The Reverend Calvert Richard Jones's photograph reveals double breechings to the quarter-deck guns with Congreve's sights and gun locks covered against the weather.

he first went to sea as the cook in a collier, published his *Treatise on Practical Seamanship,* which included useful gunnery hints from his long experience and was also written for those outside the Royal Navy. His advice was to put the oldest and best seamen to the guns' crews, let the youngsters go aloft and let the ship's boys act as powder carriers: perhaps this was the origin of *powder-monkeys.*

After 1815 it was essential to consider the lessons learnt in the long wars and listen to gunnery enthusiasts like Captain Sir Philip Bowes Vere Broke, who had victoriously commanded HM frigate *Shannon* in a short and very sharp fight with the tough US frigate *Chesapeake* in 1813. At that time, while American seamen were constantly firing at targets, British seamen 'scarcely did so once in a year'. Broke, however, exercised his guns' crews every day and is said to have fired twice a week at targets; his ship was

A howitzer: a brass 24 pdr of 1859, a type carried in ships mainly for arming their boats.

21

also always cleared for action. As the Admiralty's instructions to captains severely restricted the number of shot available for practice, some never did any. Others 'exercised the crew repeatedly in firing at marks, leaving the Gunner to account in the best manner he could for the deficiency in his stores'. That was Broke's way and it was evidently also the habit of Captain Sir Samuel John Brooke Pechell, who published *Observations on the Defective Equipment of Ship Guns* in Corfu in 1825, while on service abroad. He later became a Lord of the Admiralty and recognised the necessity for drill and an exact method. In 1818 there was a new edition of the exercise manual and in 1820 appeared *Naval Gunnery* by the son of Rear Admiral Sir Charles Douglas, who had pioneered flint-lock firing. As an artillerist Colonel Howard Douglas, who invented the refinement of a double-headed flint-lock, corresponded with officers like Broke and Pechell. His first chapter was entitled 'The Organisation and Training of Naval Gunners' and his book was still in print forty years later.

General Congreve published *A Description of the Sights or Instruments for Pointing Guns* in 1819 and his invention was adopted by the Admiralty. About 1829 their Lordships 'invited attention to the problem of the concentration of the fire of ships' broadsides...' They received suggestions for gunnery improvements from officers both active and retired. Whitehall was having to take notice and in 1830 the old third-rate HMS *Excellent*, 74 guns, Collingwood's ship at St Vincent in 1797, was designated gunnery training ship in Portsmouth harbour under the command of Captain Sir Thomas Hastings.

A gunnery student's course notebook from HMS Excellent, 1835. The drawings show the positions for crew members and their implements in spongeing and loading (centre) and firing (right), training (left).

A brig of war's 12 pdr carronade, 1829. Instead of a slide, this version has a truck carriage, as favoured by merchantmen. An apron protects the flint-lock. Etching by E. W. Cooke.

MORTAR AND CARRONADE

The Art of Throwing Bombs is the English title of a book published in French, in 1699, about siege warfare, where the need was to lob a missile over high defending walls or into a harbour where ships lay. The gun to do this was a mortar. Its shell or bomb was a hollow iron sphere, thicker at the bottom, packed with gunpowder through a hole in the top where the *fuse* was then inserted. It was designed to fall from a great height, fuse uppermost, and not to explode until it had penetrated the target. Fuses were of birch or willow wood filled with a special composition of powder, sealed into the hole with 1½ inches (38 mm) protruding, 'and then the shell is said to be *fixed*'. Mortars were put into seagoing vessels by the French as early as 1680 and were bigger than those used on land since they were usually further away from their targets.

Sea-service 10 inch (25.4 cm) and 13 inch (33 cm) mortars were fitted into the bomb-vessels which the Royal Navy adopted and the shock of their discharge was so great that special construction was needed. On a bed of great strength, carried on lower bed-beams built into the vessel, the mortar could be trained round as required. It was a *chambered* piece, the bore being much larger than the cavity which held the charge. Muller pointed out that the capacity of a 13 inch mortar was 32 pounds (14.5 kg) of powder, but that they were never charged with more than 15 pounds (6.8 kg) because the bomb-vessel is unable to bear 'the violent shock of their full charge'. Since a half-empty chamber dissipated the force of the explosion, gunners packed in all sorts of things like hay, wooden plugs and turf.

The 10 inch mortar weighed 34 cwt (1727 kg) and its fixed shell 93 pounds (41 kg), while the 13 inch weighed 81 cwt (4115 kg) and its shell was 198 pounds (90 kg). There were lugs on these shells for

Bomb-vessel with mortar, 1760; the swivel guns are for defence. The section shows the strengthened hull and the magazine racks beneath the bed. Bomb-vessels were given appropriate names like 'Infernal', 'Thunder', 'Sulphur', 'Blast' and 'Hecla'.

lifting and elaborate precautions had to be taken to protect them, especially when fixed.

The captain's cabin in the bomb-vessel served as the handling and filling room and during operations the decks were to be kept constantly watered. The cabin door was to be kept closed and covered with tanned hides to make it as secure as possible. When the mortars were firing, anti-flash precautions were even more extensive. In firing, one gunner lit the fuse as another touched off the mortar, but it was found that the flash of ignition was sufficient to light the fuse. Shells were not liked in the British navy: they were dangerous objects to have aboard although they did have their uses. Samuel Bentham, an Englishman who took service in the Imperial Russian Navy, experimented with shell guns as early as 1778.

From 1759 the Carron Company's famous iron foundry flourished beside the river Carron, near Falkirk. The company supplied guns to the Board of

Iron sea-service mortar, 10 inch (25 cm), bore weighing 18 cwt (914 kg). Its range was 1600 yards (1463 m) at 45 degrees elevation.

TOP: *Model carronade on a slide, with elevating screw. The pivot at the fore end and rollers at the after end facilitate training to left or right.*

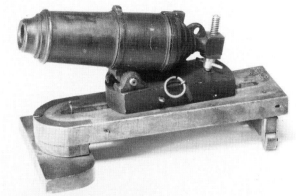

CENTRE: *HMS Victory's wooden dummy 68 pdr fo'c'sle carronade. At Trafalgar she opened with the port-side carronade firing a round-shot and a keg of 500 musket balls into the Bucentaure's stern.*

BOTTOM: *The carronade as a broadside weapon: a large elaborate model showing a variation of the slide carriage. Carronades were found in battleships until 1855.*

Ordnance in large numbers but not always satisfactorily, for in the 1770s their quality control faltered and numerous pieces failed proof. However, they were a go-ahead firm making all sorts of ironwork and had a reputation for excellence. They had their own sailing vessels to transport their products. Mr Gascoigne co-operated with General Robert Melville, whose brain-child was a short, light, chambered gun of large calibre, aptly nicknamed 'the Smasher'.

This was a cross between a cannon and a mortar, not quite a howitzer which fired high-angle shells, but more like the old cannon petro, firing at close range a big shot of low velocity which was deadly. It became known as the carronade (nearly called the gascoignade) and it certainly made its mark. Gunners knew very well that with a reduced charge a shot ploughed into the wooden hull of a ship sending great splinters flying and causing more casualties than shot that went deep or through. Opening shots in an engagement were often made with reduced charges to maim and demoralise at the outset; for the same reason, but also for penetration, guns would be double-shotted, that is loaded with two roundshot at once.

The appeal of this new weapon was twofold: it needed a much smaller gun's crew, only seven men or three in an emergency (which was an attraction for merchantmen with their smaller complements) and it needed no elaborate sighting, for it delivered its bigger shot at close range. Carronades were produced in several sizes. Carron's vessels carried them from 1778 to deter enemies who often swooped on trading vessels, even in home waters, and British privateers also bought them.

The navy soon saw their merit and adopted them as quarter-deck guns since they weighed so much less than long guns. They had some drawbacks, such as the tendency to scorch the ship's sides and rigging and the hammocks which were stowed above them. There was another disadvantage which became apparent when some ships were given all-carronade armament: their short range made it possible for an enemy to keep out of harm's way while attacking with conventional long guns. One fact which led to a great deal of argument was that carronades were not numbered among a ship's carriage guns, which seems like a great deception, but they were often replacements for swivels, which were not counted either. They were also technically different since they were mounted on *slides* not carriages.

From January 1781 there were 429 ships in the navy equipped with from four to twelve carronades more than the number of guns by which they were officially classed. In 1782 HMS *Rainbow* of 44 guns was converted entirely to carronades as an experiment and, whereas her total broadside of shot weighed 318 pounds (144 kg) before, it afterwards weighed 1238 pounds (562 kg). The largest carronades in general use were 68 pdrs, which weighed 36.5 cwt (1854 kg) and were under 5 feet (1.5 m) long; there were also 42 pdrs and 32 pdrs as well as 24, 18, 12 and 6 pdrs. Solid-cast and bored out, the carronade was not originally supported on trunnions, but on a central loop cast on the underside. It had an elevating screw instead of quoins and a dispart sight cast on the top of the reinforce ring. Its carriage was also novel, for it was a two-part slide needing, nonetheless, a stout breeching rope. When hot after repeated firing, carronades became so lively that a second rope was needed, but this was a known characteristic of guns.

HMS Bulldog firing at Bomarsund, the Russian Baltic fortress, watched by Admiral Sir Charles Napier in a sailor's straw hat. Carefully, at the correct moment, the next shell is uncased.

BIGGER GUNS AND STOUTER SHIPS

The old rivalry between the European naval powers Britain and France slumbered awhile after Napoleon went into exile, but artillerists were pondering the lessons of the war. The French believed in shell, in incendiaries and in red-hot shot heated on board ship in special furnaces. Indeed, they had lost some of their own ships by accidents involving such things. The boy who stood on the burning deck of *L'Orient* at the Battle of the Nile in 1798 was lost when that ship's magazines blew up with a staggering explosion, numbing all participants and spectators and said to have been the greater because of the shells she was carrying.

There was a curious balance between wooden ships and the number of iron shot they could absorb, something which was to be totally upset by the use of shells. After Lord Howe's Battle of the Glorious First of June 1794, a British 98 gun ship had 200 round-shot removed

from her hull and was ready for action again in a fortnight. The only ship destroyed by gunfire alone at the Battle of Trafalgar was a Spanish 74 which caught fire and blew up. Ships sometimes sank because of their battered condition, particularly in rough weather after action, but explosive shells and red-hot shot were much more formidable and once a navy had adopted them there was little rivals could do but take defensive measures and follow suit.

After 1815 Great Britain was in the position of victor, ready for any threat from any direction. Her heavy industry and technology were forging ahead but among the admirals a conservatism and faith in the old way prevailed. Meanwhile, in Paris, Colonel H-J. Paixhans published in 1822 a little book, *Nouvelle Force Maritime*, which was revolutionary enough to recommend scrapping the old warships and starting again with small steamers armed with standard large-bore

A gun's crew in action: ramming home the shot, HMS St Jean d'Acre, 1855. The 'Illustrated London News' artist has captured the determination of well drilled men at their big gun.

guns of different lengths. These fired an *obus* or shell that had its own *sabot* or wooden wad and these *canons obusiers* were chambered guns of a new design, not howitzers or carronades. Within two years the French embarked on a changeover, to be completed by 1837.

In answer to this challenge the Royal Navy, conquering its mistrust of the dangerous projectile, introduced at the beginning of Queen Victoria's reign the 8 inch (20.3 cm), 65 cwt (3302 kg) gun firing a hollow shell of 56 pounds (25.4 kg). Guns firing solid shot continued to be called by shot weight, for example 32 pounder, but shell guns were known by the bore in inches. About 1840 appeared Colonel Dundas's 68 pdr 95 cwt (4824 kg) gun firing solid shot, mounted as a pivot gun at bow and stern in certain ships, but also used as a broadside gun, on a rear-chock carriage, with its crew of nineteen men.

Firing by percussion tube and hammer

Fo'c'sle pivot gun: a 68 pdr on board HMS Immortalité at Gibraltar, 1861, drawn by E. W. Cooke. Solid shot was painted red.

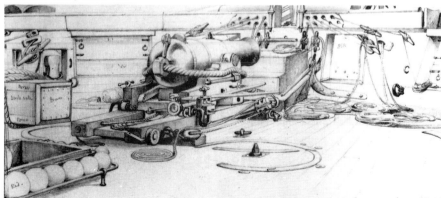

A percussion lock, 1842: the hammer was arranged to draw back on striking the priming tube, avoiding damage to the mechanism from the explosive 'rush' up the vent.

lock was introduced in 1842. A violent practical demonstration of the force of the shell was obligingly provided by a Russian fleet which destroyed a Turkish squadron in Sinope harbour in 1853. In the war of 1854-5, with France as Britain's ally against Russia in the Baltic and Crimea, there were further interesting developments. The French put their obusiers into some small 'floating batteries'. The term was not a new one but these were steam-driven vessels clad in 4½ inch (11.3 cm) iron plate and which were well able to withstand the fire from Russian forts and also to give a very good account of themselves. The large wooden three-deckers, now with auxiliary steam engines, could not get into the shallows and were vulnerable to shell from the fortifications.

After the Crimean War a 10 inch (25.4 cm) shell gun of 85 cwt (4313 kg)

A naval lieutenant with a 68 pdr 95 cwt (4826 kg) pivot gun, probably photographed in the late 1850s.

appeared and also a wrought iron 100 pdr of 125 cwt (6350 kg). This last was a compromise between the artillerists and the navy and was only half as large as designed: it was known as the Somerset after the Duke who was the First Lord of the Admiralty.

Then the French launched at Toulon in the spring of 1859 *La Gloire*, a wood-built steamer with Paixhans guns, protected by 5 inch (12.7 cm) iron cladding down to 6 feet (1.82 m) below her 250 feet (76 m) of waterline. Her builder proclaimed that against contemporary fleets she would be as a lion among a flock of sheep!

What was to be done? The Royal Navy's flagship in the Mediterranean, where Malta was the chief base, was HMS *Marlborough*, 121 guns, a larger version of Nelson's *Victory*, built in 1855 with auxiliary steam propulsion, having 8 inch (20.3 cm) shell guns on the lower and middle decks, 32 pdrs elsewhere and a 68 pdr pivot gun up for'ad.

The British Admiralty went one better: they met wood and iron with all iron, and the ship that was laid down in June 1859 at the Thames Ironworks and launched in January 1861 was to be for some years the last word. HMS *Warrior* had engines by the renowned John Penn of Greenwich, she looked like a clipper and was armour-plated with 4¹/₂ inch (114 cm) plate backed by 18

inches (45.7 cm) of teak. Her armament was twenty-six of the 68 pdrs and fourteen of an entirely new type of gun.

William G. Armstrong had been developing his invention since 1855 and not only was his construction revolutionary in that the barrel was a steel tube with wrought iron coils as reinforces fitted over it, but the breech end of the Armstrong gun was a large hollow screw through which she was loaded. With an eye on Benjamin Robins, Armstrong's barrel was rifled and his projectile was elongated with a lead skin gripped by the rifling which imparted the desired spin. There was a removable block, the vent piece, which dropped in behind charge and shot once they were 'home'; the breech screw was then wound up to seal the joint. This *rifled breech-loader* worked, and gunners made much better target practice.

HMS *Warrior* at Portsmouth mounts ten of the 110 pdr and four of the 40 pdr Armstrongs. The inventor also produced field guns, boat guns and smaller guns. Although faults in drill and in the design of the guns detracted from their reputation the *Warrior* has outlasted all and by remarkably fortunate chance she has survived to be visited today to show, in company with the *Mary Rose*, the last of the old guns at sea and the first of the new.

APPROXIMATE MEASUREMENTS OF SOME SMOOTH-BORE GUNS 1595-1859

	Length (feet)	Bore (inches)	Weight of shot (pdr)	Weight of piece (cwt)
Rabonett or robinet	3	1.75	1	2.5
Falconet or faulconet	4	2	1.5	3
Falcon or faucon	6	2.75	3	7
Minion	8	3	4	9
Saker or sacre	9	3.5	6	20
Demi-culverin, culverine or culvering	10	4	9	26
(Captured Dutch, adopted)	8.5		12	33
Culverin or culvering	11	5	18	42
(Captured Dutch, adopted)	9.5	5.8	24	47
Demi-cannon	11	6.25	32	59
Whole or cannon-of-seven	12	7	42 (out by 1790)	65
Colonel Dundas (1840)	9.5	8	68	95
Shell guns (1837)	9	8	56	65
The 'Somerset' (1859)	8.75	10	100	125
Carronades (1779)				
from 12 pdrs up, e.g.	3.25		18	10
	5.4	8	68	36.5

HMS Warrior today: number 14 broadside gun, an Armstrong 110 pdr on a rear-chock carriage showing the hollow breech screw for loading.

FURTHER READING

Blackmore, H. L. *The Armouries of the Tower of London* (catalogue), volume 1 'Ordnance', and appendices 'Ordnance in Ancient Monuments and on Loan' and 'Dimensions, Weights and Ranges of Ordnance 1455-1868'. HMSO, 1976.

Carpenter, A. C. *Cannon of Pendennis and St Mawes Castles.* Privately published and available from the author, Ivybridge, Devon PL21 0AQ.

Caruana, A. B. *The History of English Sea Ordnance.* Volume I, 1523-1715. Volume II, 1715-1815. Rotherfield, Jean Boudriot, 1994 and 1997.

Douglas, Sir H. *A Treatise on Naval Gunnery.* London, 1855. Reprinted by Conway Maritime Press, 1982.

Garbett, Captain H. *Naval Gunnery.* London, 1897. Reprinted by SR Publishing, Wakefield, 1971.

Hogg, I., and Batchelor, J. *Naval Gun.* Blandford, 1978.

Hughes, Major-General B. P. *British Smooth-Bore Artillery.* Arms and Armour Press, 1969.

Hutchinson, W. *A Treatise on Practical Seamanship.* London, 1777. Reprinted by Scolar Maritime Library, 1979.

Jackson, M. H., and de Beer, C. *Eighteenth Century Gunfounding.* David & Charles, 1973.

Kaestlin, Major J. P. (editor). *Museum of Artillery* (catalogue), volume 1 'Ordnance'. HMSO, revised edition 1970.

Kennard, A. N. *Gunfounding and Gunfounders.* Arms and Armour Press, 1986.

Lavery, Brian. *The Arming and Fitting of English Ships of War 1600-1815.* Conway, 1987. A most comprehensive and detailed survey.

Mariner's Mirror. Quarterly journal of the Society for Nautical Research. Volume 1, 1911, continuing. Many authoritative articles, as: volume 38 (1952), page 301, J. D. Moody, 'Old Naval Gun-carriages'; volume 72 (1986), page 439, F. Howard, 'Early Ship Guns: I. Built-up Breech-Loaders'; volume 73 (1987), page 49, 'Early Ship Guns: II Swivels'; volume 82 (1996), page 269, G. Parker, 'The Dreadnought Revolution of Tudor England', and page 301, N. A. M. Rodger, 'The Development of Broadside Gunnery 1450-1650'.

Mountaine, William. *The Seaman's Vade Mecum and Defensive War by Sea*. London, 1756. Reprinted by Conway Maritime Press, 1971.

Muller, J. *A Treatise of Artillery*. London, 1780. Reprinted, Ottawa, 1965.

Nautical Archaeology and Underwater Exploration, International Journal of. Volume 1, 1972, continuing.

Padfield, P. *Guns at Sea*. Hugh Evelyn, 1973.

Robins, B. *New Principles of Gunnery*. London, 1742. Reprinted by Richmond Publishing Company, 1972.

Rule, M. *The Mary Rose. The Excavation and Raising of Henry VIII's Flagship*. Conway Maritime Press, 1985.

Seller, John. *The Sea Gunner 1691* (facsimile reprint). Rotherfield, Jean Boudriot, 1994.

Slaymaker, E. F. 'The Armament of HMS *Warrior*', *Warship* numbers 37, 38 *et seq.*, 1986.

Smith, Captain John. *A Seaman's Grammar*. London, 1627. Reprinted (edited by K. Goell), Michael Joseph, 1970.

Stewart, R., and Heyes, D. *Scale Model Cannon*. John Murray, 1982.

Warship. Published quarterly, Conway Maritime Press.

Wells, J. G. *The Immortal Warrior: Britain's First and Last Battleship*. Kenneth Mason, 1987.

PLACES TO VISIT

In addition to the major centres below there are naval guns and related items in most museums in seaport towns and specialist maritime museums. Many castles and fortresses also have examples of guns which are virtually the same as sea-service weapons (see H. L. Blackmore under further reading). Intending visitors are advised to find out times of opening before making a special journey.

The Armouries, HM Tower of London, Tower Hill, London EC3N 4AB. Telephone: 0171-480 6358.

Chatham Historic Dockyard, Chatham, Kent ME4 4TE. Telephone: 01634 812551.

Museum of Artillery in the Rotunda, Repository Road, Woolwich, London SE18. Telephone: 0181-316 5402.

National Maritime Museum, Romney Road, Greenwich, London SE10 9NF. Telephone: 0181-858 4422.

Royal Naval Museum, HM Naval Base, Portsmouth, Hampshire PO1 3NU. Telephone: 01705 733060, extension 23868. See here the *Mary Rose* Ship Hall, HMS *Victory*, HMS *Warrior*.

Science Museum, Exhibition Road, South Kensington, London SW7 2DD. Telephone: 0171-938 8000.

Scottish United Services Museum, The Castle, Edinburgh EH1 2NG. Telephone: 0131-225 7534.

Southsea Castle and Museum, Clarence Esplanade, Southsea, Portsmouth, Hampshire PO5 3PA. Telephone: 01705 827261.